Thinking of You

Thinking of You

Thinking of You

Thinking of You

_____

Thinking of You

Thinking of You

_____

Thinking of You

Thinking of You

_____

Thinking of You

_____

Thinking of You

_____

Thinking of You

Thinking of You

_____

Thinking of You

_____

Thinking of You

Thinking of You

Thinking of You

_____

Thinking of You

Thinking of You

_____

Thinking of You

_____

Thinking of You

_____

Thinking of You

Thinking of You

_____

Thinking of You

Thinking of You

_____

Thinking of You

_____

Thinking of You

_____

Thinking of You

_____

Thinking of You

Thinking of You

Thinking of You

Thinking of You

_____

Thinking of You

Thinking of You

_____

_____

_____

_____

_____

_____

_____

_____

_____

_____

_____

_____

_____

_____

_____

_____

_____

_____

_____

_____

_____

Thinking of You

Thinking of You

Thinking of You

Thinking of You

Thinking of You

Thinking of You

_____

Thinking of You

Thinking of You

Thinking of You

_____

Thinking of You

Thinking of You

Thinking of You

Thinking of You

_____

_____

_____

_____

_____

_____

_____

_____

_____

_____

_____

_____

_____

_____

_____

_____

_____

_____

_____

_____

_____

_____

Thinking of You

Thinking of You

_____

Thinking of You

_____

Thinking of You

_____

Thinking of You

Thinking of You

Thinking of You

_____

Thinking of You

_____

Thinking of You

Thinking of You

Thinking of You

_____

Thinking of You

_____

_____

_____

_____

_____

_____

_____

_____

_____

_____

_____

_____

_____

_____

_____

_____

_____

_____

_____

_____

_____

_____

_____

Thinking of You

Thinking of You

Thinking of You

_____

Thinking of You

Thinking of You

Thinking of You

_____

Thinking of You

Thinking of You

Thinking of You

_____

Thinking of You

Thinking of You

Thinking of You

Thinking of You

Thinking of You

Thinking of You

Thinking of You

Thinking of You

_____

Thinking of You

Thinking of You

Thinking of You

_____

Thinking of You

_____

Thinking of You

Thinking of You

_____

_____

_____

_____

_____

_____

_____

_____

_____

_____

_____

_____

_____

_____

_____

_____

_____

_____

_____

_____

_____

_____

_____

_____

Thinking of You

_____

Thinking of You

Thinking of You

Thinking of You

Thinking of You

Thinking of You

Thinking of You

Thinking of You

Thinking of You

_____

Thinking of You

Thinking of You

Thinking of You

_____

Thinking of You

Thinking of You

Thinking of You

Thinking of You

Thinking of You

_____

Thinking of You

_____

Thinking of You

_____

Made in the USA
Las Vegas, NV
27 April 2023

71177606R00056